How many chicks?

Shelley Davidow

This is Ben.
He has a white hen.

The white hen has
a small house.

This is Mary.
She has three brown hens.

The brown hens have
a big house.

Mary and Ben are in the classroom.
The teacher draws a hen.

Who has hens?
I have a white hen.
I have three brown hens.

I have one white hen
and two yellow chicks!

I have three brown hens
and six yellow chicks!

What is that?
It is a chick.

Who has chicks?

We have!

First published 1998 by
MACMILLAN EDUCATION LTD
London and Basingstoke
Companies and representatives throughout the world

ISBN 0–333–71720-1

10 9 8 7 6 5 4 3 2 1
07 06 05 04 03 02 01 00 99 98

This book is printed on paper suitable for recycling and made from fully managed and sustained forest sources.

Typeset by Tek-Art, Croydon, Surrey

Printed in Hong Kong

A catalogue record for this book is available from the British Library.

Illustrations by Annabel Large/B.L. Kearley Ltd